Gold Stars®
English
AGES
9-11
Key Stage 2
Parragon
Bath • New York • Cologne • Melbourne • Delhi
Hong Kong • Shenzhen • Singapore • Amsterdam
D0351877

This edition published by Parragon Books Ltd in 2014

Parragon Books Ltd
Chartist House
15–17 Trim Street
Bath BA1 1HA, UK
www.parragon.com

Written by Nina Filipek
Educational consultant: Martin Malcolm
Illustrated by Rob Davis/www.the-art-agency.co.uk
and Tom Connell/www.the-art-agency.co.uk

ISBN 978-1-4723-6038-0

Printed in China

Parents' notes

The Gold Stars Key Stage 2 series

The Gold Stars Key Stage 2 series has been created to help your child revise and practise key skills and information learned in school. Each book is a complete companion to the Key Stage 2 curriculum and has been written by an expert team of teachers. The books will help to prepare your child for the SATs tests that they take in Year 6 and other tests that they take at school.

The books also support Scottish National Guidelines 5-14.

How to use this workbook

- Talk through the introductions to each topic and review the examples together.
- Encourage your child to tackle the fill-in activities independently.
- Keep work times short. Skip a page if it seems too difficult and return to it later.
- It doesn't matter if your child does some of the pages out of order.
- Your child does not need to answer the questions in complete sentences.
- Check the answers on pages 60-63. Encourage effort and reward achievement with praise.
- If your child finds any of the pages too difficult, don't worry. Children learn at different rates.

Contents

Spelling, grammar and punctuation

Reading comprehension

Fiction

Writing composition

Spelling tips

Learning objective: to know about different spelling methods

There are lots of things you can do to help with your spelling.

Learn words in groups. For example:

bright fright might sight

Look for words within words, or words that have a common root. For example:

sign signal signature

Keep a spelling log of difficult words. For example, any with silent letters, such as:

knife comb cupboard

Look, say, cover, write, check:

- look at the word
- say it out loud
- cover it with one hand
- write it without looking
- check it

Did you get it right?

Break longer words into syllables. For example:

information = in/form/a/tion

Use a mnemonic. For example:

'Necessary' has one coffee with two sugars (there are one c and two s's in the word).

Say the word as it is spelt.

Learning the short words first will help you to spell the longer words later.

A

Look at the words below. Can you see any short words within them? Write the short words next to the long words.

caterpillar	cat pill ate ill pillar	supermarket	______
television	______	subway	______
cupboard	______	basketball	______
wardrobe	______	crossword	______

Some words, called homophones, sound the same but are spelt differently. For example:

bus fare	fire grate	horse's rein
fair ground	great fun	rain water

DEFINITION

mnemonic: A method to help you remember something, e.g. 'i' comes before 'e' except after 'c'.

syllable: The beats in a word are syllables. Words with only one beat are monosyllabic.

B

Read the passage below. Cross out any wrong spellings and write the correct spellings above.

On Saturday, we tuck the train into town. We usually go bye car because Mum

says the train fair is two deer, but she agrees it's much faster bye train.

We even had a drink on the train, witch we can't do in the car! We didn't

knead to pay four parking either so I think the train was cheeper in the end!

Spelling plurals

Learning objective: to learn to spell plurals

Nouns (people, places and things) can be either singular or plural.

For example:

one dog (singular)

two dogs (plural)

Remember!
To make most words plural, you just add an 's'.

Learning the rules will help you to spell plurals.

A

1. To make some nouns plural, you just add an 's'. Add an 's' to the end of these nouns to make them plural.

banana__ girl__ boy__ day__ star__

2. To make some other nouns plural, you add 'es'. Write 'es' at the end of these nouns to make them plural.

potato___ bus___ box___ dish___
watch___ dress___ tomato___ brush___
bench___ glass___ wish___ volcano___

Remember!
When nouns end in 'ch', 'sh', 's', 'ss' or 'x' add 'es' to make them plural. When a noun ends in 'o' we also usually add 'es'.

DEFINITION

singular: A singular word indicates that there is just one thing.

plural: A plural word indicates that there is more than one thing.

Parents' notes

The Gold Stars Key Stage 2 series

The Gold Stars Key Stage 2 series has been created to help your child revise and practise key skills and information learned in school. Each book is a complete companion to the Key Stage 2 curriculum and has been written by an expert team of teachers. The books will help to prepare your child for the SATs tests that they take in Year 6 and other tests that they take at school.

The books also support Scottish National Guidelines 5-14.

How to use this workbook

- Talk through the introductions to each topic and review the examples together.
- Encourage your child to tackle the fill-in activities independently.
- Keep work times short. Skip a page if it seems too difficult and return to it later.
- It doesn't matter if your child does some of the pages out of order.
- Your child does not need to answer the questions in complete sentences.
- Check the answers on pages 60-63. Encourage effort and reward achievement with praise.
- If your child finds any of the pages too difficult, don't worry. Children learn at different rates.

Contents

Spelling, grammar and punctuation

Reading comprehension

Fiction

Writing composition

Spelling tips

Learning objective: to know about different spelling methods

There are lots of things you can do to help with your spelling.

Learn words in groups. For example:

bright fright might sight

Look for words within words, or words that have a common root. For example:

sign signal signature

Keep a spelling log of difficult words. For example, any with silent letters, such as:

knife comb cupboard

Look, say, cover, write, check:

- look at the word
- say it out loud
- cover it with one hand
- write it without looking
- check it

Did you get it right?

Break longer words into syllables. For example:

information = in/form/a/tion

Use a mnemonic. For example:

'Necessary' has one coffee with two sugars (there are one c and two s's in the word).

Say the word as it is spelt.

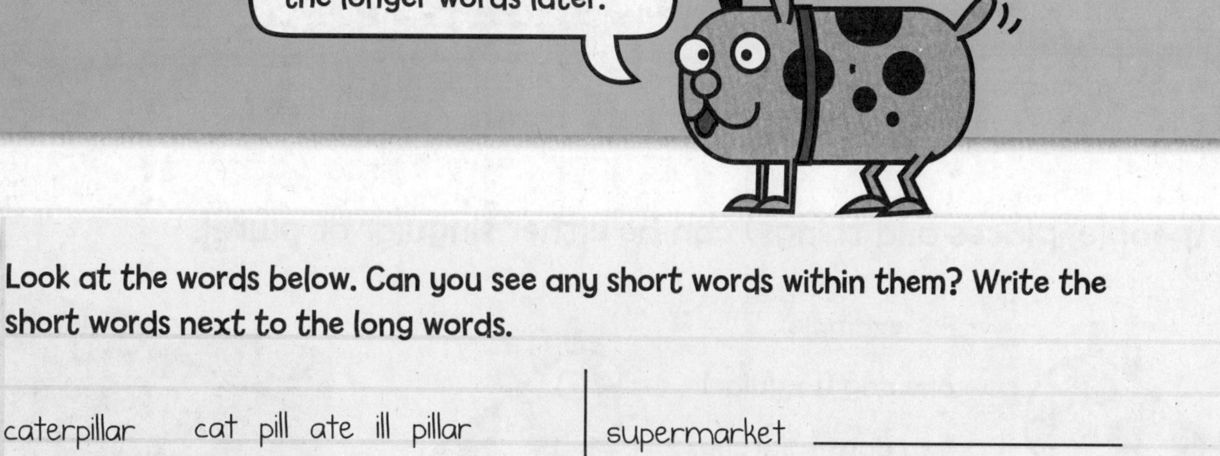

A

Look at the words below. Can you see any short words within them? Write the short words next to the long words.

caterpillar	cat pill ate ill pillar	supermarket	________
television	________	subway	________
cupboard	________	basketball	________
wardrobe	________	crossword	________

Some words, called homophones, sound the same but are spelt differently. For example:

bus fare	fire grate	horse's rein
fair ground	great fun	rain water

DEFINITION

mnemonic: A method to help you remember something, e.g. 'i' comes before 'e' except after 'c'.

syllable: The beats in a word are syllables. Words with only one beat are monosyllabic.

B

Read the passage below. Cross out any wrong spellings and write the correct spellings above.

On Saturday, we tuck the train into town. We usually go bye car because Mum says the train fair is two deer, but she agrees it's much faster bye train. We even had a drink on the train, witch we can't do in the car! We didn't knead to pay four parking either so I think the train was cheeper in the end!

Spelling plurals

Learning objective: to learn to spell plurals

Nouns (people, places and things) can be either singular or plural.

For example:

one dog (singular)

two dogs (plural)

Remember!
To make most words plural, you just add an 's'.

Learning the rules will help you to spell plurals.

A

1. To make some nouns plural, you just add an 's'. Add an 's' to the end of these nouns to make them plural.

banana__ girl__ boy__ day__ star__

2. To make some other nouns plural, you add 'es'. Write 'es' at the end of these nouns to make them plural.

potato___ bus___ box___ dish___

watch___ dress___ tomato___ brush___

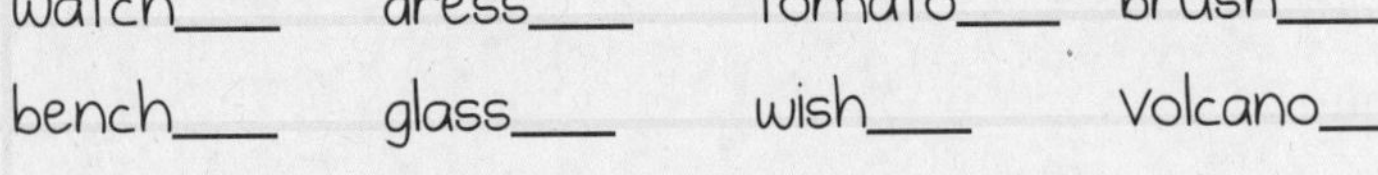

bench___ glass___ wish___ volcano___

DEFINITION

singular: A singular word indicates that there is just one thing.

plural: A plural word indicates that there is more than one thing.

Remember!

When nouns end in 'ch', 'sh', 's', 'ss' or 'x' add 'es' to make them plural. When a noun ends in 'o' we also usually add 'es'.

B

1. **When a noun ends in an 'f' sound, drop the 'f' and write 'ves'. Write these nouns as plurals.**

leaf > lea ________ knife > kni ________ calf > cal ________

2. **When a noun ends in a consonant followed by a 'y', drop the 'y' and write 'ies'. Have a go at these.**

baby > ________ butterfly > ________ pony > ________
story > ________ party > ________ lady > ________

Some plurals don't follow the rules. You will need to learn these separately.

mouse > mice tooth > teeth man > men

3. **Write the plurals for these tricky nouns. You can use a dictionary to help you.**

goose > ________ sheep > ________ deer > ________
foot > ________ child > ________ woman > ________

Prefixes and suffixes

Learning objective: to learn about prefixes and suffixes

A prefix is a letter (or group of letters) added to the beginning of a word.
A suffix is a letter (or group of letters) added to the end of a word.

A

1. **Add the missing prefix or suffix. Tele means 'far away'. Auto means 'by itself'.**

Another word for your signature auto ________
A long tube with a lens at the end tele ________
Something that works by itself ________matic
Another word for car auto ________
Something that allows you to speak to someone far away tele ________
Your own life story, written by you ________biography

2. **Sometimes a prefix is added to change the meaning of a word. If the prefix 'anti' means 'not', what do you think these words mean? Write your definitions.**

anti-ageing ________________________________
anti-bacterial ________________________________
anti-freeze ________________________________

B

Which of these things would you expect to find in toothpaste? Circle your answer.

anti-ageing cream

an anti-bacterial ingredient

anti-freeze

So, 'anti-' isn't the same as 'aunty' then?!

C

Add the missing suffixes. Choose from 'cian' or 'ist'. Then write a definition for each one.

Word	Meaning
magician	Someone who performs magic tricks
pian ______	
chem______	
beauti______	
electri ______	
musi______	
politi ______	
biolog______	

A suffix can change a word from singular to plural, but can also change a verb (an action word) into a noun.

verb		noun
paint	→	painter
dance	→	dancer

D

Add the suffix 'er' to change these verbs into nouns.

verb	noun
sing	
garden	
teach	
climb	
walk	
play	

Punctuation

Learning objective: to learn to use basic punctuation

We use punctuation to show the reader how words should be spoken and to help them understand the text.

Commas tell readers to pause and take a moment to understand what a sentence is about. Put a comma after each item of a list. Put a comma after a group of words that belong together. Never put a comma before the word 'and'.

A **Write the missing commas in these sentences.**

When Superboy whispered a secret word his school jumper became a long shiny red cloak and his spectacles morphed into a mirrored black mask. His super-human powers enabled him to climb vertical walls scale rooftops sense danger and bring wrong-doers to justice.

Exclamation marks (!) are used to signal surprise, excitement or humour.

B **Read the passage below and write in exclamation marks or full stops where they are missing.**

All of a sudden, the rock door split open and a dark figure sprang out It was the Evil Weevil, Superboy's deadliest enemy Weevil eyed him menacingly for a second and lunged forward with a blood-curdling battle cry

DEFINITION

punctuation marks: These are commas, full stops, exclamation marks, apostrophes, etc – the punctuation we use to make our writing clearer to the reader.

exclaim: This means 'to cry out'. Hence we say 'exclamation mark'.

Question marks (?) are used to signal a question.

C **Write a question mark at the end of the sentences where questions are asked. If a sentence is not a question, you can use either a full stop or an exclamation mark.**

How was Superboy going to defeat the Evil Weevil Was he cunning and clever enough to outwit him Everyone knew that the Weevil was a wimp really but he was a scary wimp, all the same What would happen if Superboy failed Would the Earth be plunged into another inter-planetary war

Remember!

Sentences that ask questions usually begin with Who, What, When, Where, How, Why or Can.

Speech marks are drawn around any words that are spoken.

D **Write the speech marks in the dialogue below.**

So, Superboy, we meet at last, the Weevil sneered. It's a shame we don't have time to strike up a friendship! Ha, ha, ha! The Weevil laughed at his own feeble joke.

I wouldn't worry, Weevil, replied Superboy. You'll have plenty of time to make friends with the cockroaches you'll meet in the state planetary prison!

Remember!

- Speech marks open at the start and close at the end of the words spoken.
- All other punctuation goes inside the speech marks.
- Start a new paragraph for each new speaker.

More punctuation

Learning objective: to learn to use apostrophes, colons and ellipses

Apostrophes are a form of punctuation that can be used in two different ways.

When an apostrophe is used to shorten a word it is known as a contraction. Apostrophes can also be used to show possession.

Examples of contractions:	Examples of possessive words:
do not = don't	Sally's shoes
can not = can't	The dog's dinner
we are = we're	My sister's dress

Do you know the difference between possessive apostrophes and contractions?

A

In the sentences below, circle the apostrophes that shorten words and underline the apostrophes that show possession.

1. I can't find it. It's gone!
2. That's my friend's house.
3. It's Toni's book.
4. Where's Mrs Dale's class?
5. They'll be late for school.
6. We're going to Gina's party.

B

Write these contractions in full.

can't > ____________________

it's > ____________________

that's > ____________________

they'll > ____________________

where's > ____________________

we're > ____________________

With an apostrophe, 'it's' is a contraction that means 'it has' or 'it is'. Without an apostrophe, 'its' is used to show possession.

Examples of contractions with 'it's':	Examples of the possessive 'its':
I think it's been raining.	The dog buried its bone.
It's warm outside today.	The sweet stuck to its wrapper.
It's nearly lunchtime.	The door fell off its hinges.

For example, when there is more than one dog you say:
The dogs' dinners.

In plural nouns, possessive apostrophes come after the 's'.

C

Put possessive apostrophes in these sentences.

1. The clowns car fell apart. (one clown)
2. The clowns car fell apart. (two clowns)
3. The dogs owner went to the Pooch Parlour. (one dog)
4. The dogs owner went to the Pooch Parlour. (two dogs)
5. The girls rabbit ran away. (one girl)
6. The girls rabbit ran away. (two girls)
7. The mans sunglasses were expensive. (one man)
8. The mens sunglasses were expensive. (two men)

Remember!
There are some exceptions to the rules.
For example:
children = children's
men = men's

DEFINITION

contraction: A word formed by omitting (leaving out) or combining some of the sounds of a longer phrase.

These are some of the other punctuation marks you are likely to come across:

Pauses are marked with ellipses...
"I'd like a burger, fries and... ummm, an ice cream, please," said Emma.

Ellipses can also be used to show that words are missing.
"He left the room, banged the door...and went out."

Lists start with a colon:
The meal deal includes: a whopper burger, mega-fries and a drink.

Clauses and conjunctions

Learning objective: to learn about clauses and conjunctions

A clause is a group of words with a subject (a noun) and a verb. A sentence always has at least one clause.

For example:

The show ended. (one clause)	'the show' = noun	'ended' = verb
The audience clapped loudly. (one clause)	'the audience' = noun	'clapped' = verb

Two or more clauses can be joined in a sentence.

For example:

The show ended and the audience clapped loudly.

Or:

The audience clapped loudly when the show ended.

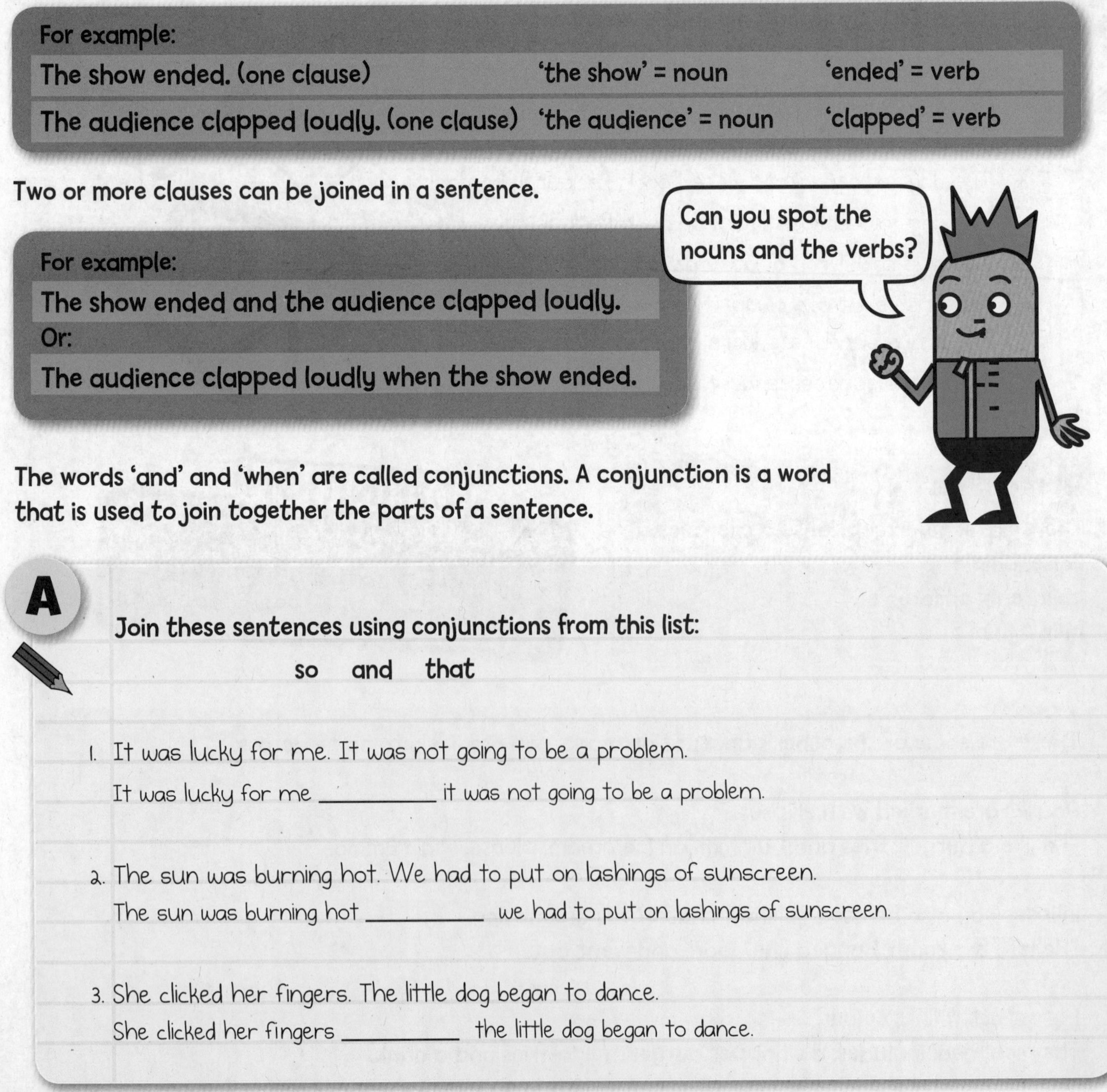

The words 'and' and 'when' are called conjunctions. A conjunction is a word that is used to join together the parts of a sentence.

A

Join these sentences using conjunctions from this list:

so and that

1. It was lucky for me. It was not going to be a problem.
   It was lucky for me __________ it was not going to be a problem.

2. The sun was burning hot. We had to put on lashings of sunscreen.
   The sun was burning hot __________ we had to put on lashings of sunscreen.

3. She clicked her fingers. The little dog began to dance.
   She clicked her fingers __________ the little dog began to dance.

DEFINITION

noun: A word for a person, place or thing.

verb: A word for an action.

Connectives are words that link together ideas, sentences and paragraphs.

Here are some examples of connectives:

first next finally consequently later suddenly except
meanwhile however when but after although also

B

Underline the connectives.

First, we went to the Tower of London to see the Crown Jewels. Next, we saw Big Ben and, after lunch, we had a great time at the London Dungeon. Although it rained for most of the day we didn't really notice, except when we finally got back to the bus station and had to wait ages for the bus to come... in the rain!

C

Choose from these connectives to complete the passage below:

next first lastly but then

__________ we went on the Ghost Train. It wasn't as scary as we thought it was going to be. __________ __________ we went on the Rocky Coaster and that was terrifying! We thought we were going to go flying off the track! __________ we got a real soaking on the Log Flume and the Crazy Rapids. __________ we had a ride on the Angry Camel and it was so funny that we couldn't stop laughing.

Pronouns

Learning objective: to understand how to use pronouns

A noun is a person, place or thing. A pronoun is used to replace a noun so that you don't have to repeat it.

For example, the second of these two sentences uses the pronoun 'he' instead of repeating 'Mr Parker':

Mr Parker is strict but Mr Parker makes us laugh.

Mr Parker is strict but he makes us laugh.

A

Choosing from the list below, change the underlined nouns to pronouns. Cross out the noun and write the pronoun above it.

I me you he him she
her we us they them it

1. Mr Parker gave Class 5 a detention so Class 5 missed their playtime.
2. Our class won the merit prize so our class are going on a trip to the zoo.
3. Chris is team captain because Chris is the best at football.
4. Katie loves swimming so Katie joined the swimming club.
5. I usually like history but today history was boring.
6. We watched a film about spiders because we were doing a topic on spiders.

DEFINITION

pronoun: A word that is used to replace a noun.

possess: This means to own something. Hence we say 'possessive pronoun'.

Possessive pronouns show ownership (or possession).

B Complete the sentences by choosing possessive pronouns from the list.

mine his hers yours theirs ours its

1. It belongs to me. It's ________.
2. This belongs to you. This is ________.
3. The coats belong to them. The coats are ________.
4. The cat belongs to her. The cat is ________.
5. The dog eats the dinner that belongs to it. The dog eats ________ dinner.

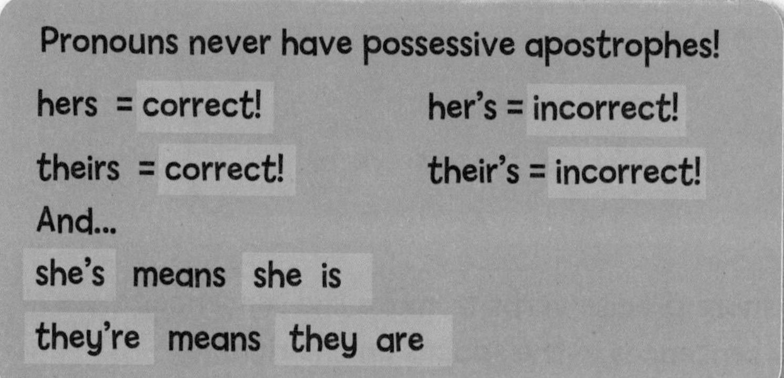

Pronouns never have possessive apostrophes!

hers = correct! her's = incorrect!

theirs = correct! their's = incorrect!

And...

she's means she is

they're means they are

C Write three sentences of your own using different pronouns.

1.

2.

3.

Verbs and adverbs

Learning objective: to learn how to use verbs and adverbs

Verbs and adverbs bring action and pace to your writing. Choose them carefully!

A **Write the past tense for each of these verbs.**

I draw → I ______

I write → I ______

I swim → I ______

I catch → I ______

I see → I ______

I go → I ______

Remember!
A verb is an action word.

You can improve your writing by choosing verbs that give precise, rather than general, information.

For example:	
The giant ate the cakes.	(ate = general verb)
The giant gobbled up the cakes.	(gobbled = precise verb)

B **Replace the underlined verbs below with more precise verbs to make the sentences more interesting for the reader. Write the new sentences in the spaces on the right.**

1. The giant walked across the room. 1. ______
2. "Hubble, bubble, toil and trouble," said the witch. 2. ______
3. The elf went into the shop. 3. ______
4. The vampire got out of the coffin. 4. ______
5. The wizard made a potion. 5. ______

Adverbs usually answer questions, such as How? Where? or When?

Many adverbs end in -ly.

For example:

The giant immediately gobbled up the sweets. immediately = adverb

Here are some examples of adverbs:

really easily poorly deeply plainly

clearly happily angrily badly fiercely

C Add an adverb to each sentence. Use your own ideas, or choose from this list:

quietly carefully suddenly quickly angrily menacingly

1. The giant stomped ____________ across the room.
2. "Hubble, bubble, toil and trouble," cackled the witch ____________.
3. The elf sneaked ____________ into the shop.
4. The vampire ____________ leaped out of the coffin.
5. The wizard ____________ concocted a potion.
6. The boy ____________ snatched the wand.

DEFINITION

adverb: An adverb gives more meaning and explanation to the verb.

past tense: The form of the word that tells us something happened in the past.

Remember!
An adverb can change the meaning of a sentence.

Adjectives and metaphors

Learning objective: to learn how to use adjectives, metaphors and similes

An adjective describes a noun.

Clever use of adjectives can make your writing more exciting.

The adjectives in the second sentence tell the reader more about the bird and the nest.

For example:

The bird swooped down from its nest.

bird = noun　　nest = noun　　swooped = precise verb

The rare, golden-feathered bird swooped down from its rocky nest.

rare, golden-feathered, rocky = adjectives

A **Make these sentences more exciting for the reader by adding adjectives. Write the new sentences on the lines below.**

1. The car raced round the track.

___

2. The pony jumped the fence.

___

3. The chef cooked a meal.

___

4. The plane landed on the runway.

___

5. The artist painted a picture.

___

Describe one thing as if it really is something else and you are using a metaphor.

Example of a metaphor:
The moon is a silver mirror.

B **Write down what you think these metaphors mean.**

1. Joe's a sly fox! ____________________

2. Jen's a rock. ____________________

Describe one thing as if it is like something else and you are using a simile.

Examples of similes:
The giant's hands were like great shovels.
His feet were as big as boats!

C **Write your own similes to complete these sentences about a terrible troll. The first one has been done for you.**

1. His hair looked like... a bird's nest.
2. His teeth were like... ____________
3. His nose was like a... ____________
4. His toes were like... ____________

D **Complete these well-known similes.**

1. As hard as... ____________
2. As strong as an... ____________
3. As weak as a... ____________
4. As white as a... ____________
5. As cold as... ____________
6. As red as a... ____________

Word play

Learning objective: to know about proverbs, idioms and onomatopoeia

You can brighten up your writing or add humour by playing with words.

A proverb is a well-known saying that expresses a comment on life.

A

Explain what you think each proverb means.

1. Practice makes perfect. ____________________
2. A stitch in time saves nine. ____________________
3. Look before you leap. ____________________
4. Don't look a gift horse in the mouth. ____________________
5. Too many cooks spoil the broth. ____________________

Remember!
Many proverbs are also metaphors.

An idiom is something people often say, where the message is different from the actual meaning of the words.

B

Find out what these idioms mean and write a definition for each one.

1. I'm feeling under the weather. ____________________
2. He had egg on his face. ____________________
3. It's raining cats and dogs. ____________________
4. We're cooking on gas. ____________________

Onomatopoeia is when a word echoes the sound it is describing.

For example:

pop! clash! smash! bash!

C

Complete each sentence with an appropriate onomatopoeia. Choose from:

pop fizzed buzzed squelched thud smashed crashed

1. The balloon burst with a loud ______________.
2. The glass ______________ onto the floor.
3. My feet ______________ in thick mud.
4. The heavy door closed with a ______________.
5. The bees ______________ around the flowers.
6. The waves ______________ onto the rocks.
7. The drink ______________ in the can.

DEFINITION

onomatopoeia: A word that actually sounds like the word it is describing.

collective noun: A word for a group of things, e.g. choir, team, pack.

D

Do some research and complete these collective nouns. Choose from the list below:

cows dolphins geese wolves lions birds bees

1. A gaggle of ______________
2. A pack of ______________
3. A pride of ______________
4. A herd of ______________
5. A flock of ______________
6. A swarm of ______________
7. A school of ______________

Remember!
Using a collective noun is a more interesting way of writing about a group of animals.

First, second and third person

Learning objective: to understand about first, second and third person writing

There are three main types of writing – first, second and third person.

Writing in the first person means using the pronouns I, my, mine and we.

First person is usually used for:
- diaries and letters
- personal accounts of events, activities and visits
- autobiographies
- stories told by the leading character

Writing in the second person means addressing the reader directly, using the pronoun you.

Second person is usually used for:
- advertisements
- instructions and directions
- discussion texts

Writing in the third person means using the pronouns he, she, it and they.

Third person is usually used for:
- novels and stories
- information texts
- news reports

first person: When someone writes about himself or herself.
second person: When someone writes to address you as the reader.
third person: When someone writes about someone or something else (e.g. he, she, it, they).

Look for examples of first, second and third person text in comics, magazines and newspapers.

A

Read the three pieces of writing below and decide whether they are written in the first person, second person or third person. Underline the pronouns to help you decide. Then write 1st, 2nd or 3rd in the box next to each extract.

1. Palm-fringed beaches and turquoise waters await you on this Caribbean dream holiday. You can enjoy five-star luxury with classic elegance at the Fabulossi Hotel for only $1,000 per person, including flights.

2. Emily felt betrayed. Lisa was her best friend. They'd been friends since they were four years old and at nursery together. But now she'd seen a note written on a page in Lisa's Pony Diary: 'Number one best friend: Becky. Number two best friend: Emily.'

3. Just when I thought it couldn't get any better, we scored again. It was a 3-0 hat-trick with only a minute left! Everyone around me went wild, including my dad. It was the best feeling ever!

B

Now rewrite the text from extract 2 in the first person.

Classic fiction

Learning objective: to learn how to extract information from a classic text

This is an extract from a book called Treasure Island. Read it twice, carefully.

... I was far less afraid of the captain himself than anybody else who knew him. There were nights when he took a good deal more rum and water than his head would carry; and then he would sometimes sit and sing his wicked, old sea-songs, minding nobody.

But sometimes he would call for glasses round, and force all the trembling company to listen to his stories or bear a chorus to his singing. Often I have heard the house shaking with "Yo-ho-ho, and a bottle of rum", all the neighbours joining in for dear life, with the fear of death upon them, each singing louder than the other to avoid remark.

For in these fits he was the most over-riding companion ever known. He would slap his hand on the table for silence all round. He would fly up in a passion of anger at a question, or sometimes because none was put, and so he judged the company was not following his story. Nor would he allow anyone to leave the inn till he had drunk himself sleepy and reeled off to bed.

Robert Louis Stevenson (1850–94)

DEFINITION

sea-song: A song that sailors might sing.
over-riding: A person who is extremely loud, bossy and forceful towards others.

A

Use the text on page 28 to answer these questions.

1. Was the person telling the story afraid of the captain?

2. What kind of person was the captain?

3. What did he do when he drank too much?

4. Why did everyone sing so loudly? Explain your answer.

5. What made the captain angry?

6. Why did he slap his hand on the table?

7. Do you think the person telling the story knows the captain well?

Classic poetry

Learning objective: to read and understand a classic poem

This is an extract from a poem called **Upon a Snail**. Read it twice, carefully.

Upon a Snail

She goes but softly, but she goeth sure,
She stumbles not, as stronger creatures do;
Her journey's shorter, so she may endure
Better than they which do much further go.

She makes no noise, but stilly seizeth on
The flower or herb appointed for her food;
The which she quietly doth feed upon,
While others range, and glare, but find no good.

And though she doth but very softly go,
However slow her pace be, yet 'tis sure;
And certainly they that do travel so,
The prize which they do aim at, they procure.

John Bunyan (1628–88)

DEFINITION

goeth: goes
to endure: to keep going
stilly: quietly
seizeth: takes hold of
herb: green plant or leaf
doth: does
range: travel far
glare: stare searchingly
pace: speed
'tis: it is
procure: gain or win

For activities about writing poetry, see page 46 of this workbook.

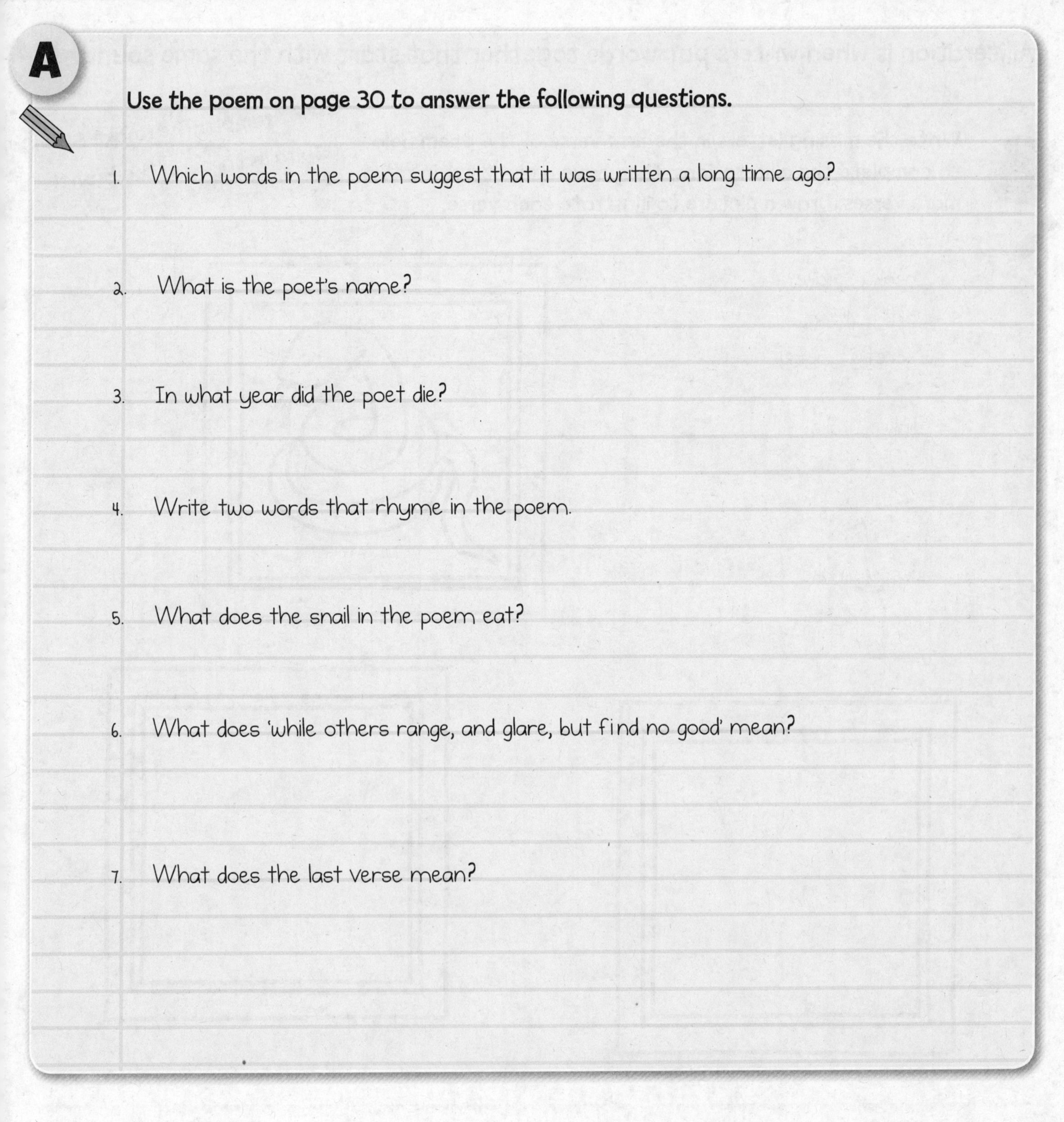

A

Use the poem on page 30 to answer the following questions.

1. Which words in the poem suggest that it was written a long time ago?

2. What is the poet's name?

3. In what year did the poet die?

4. Write two words that rhyme in the poem.

5. What does the snail in the poem eat?

6. What does 'while others range, and glare, but find no good' mean?

7. What does the last verse mean?

Poetry: alliteration and rhyme

Learning objective: to be able to recognize alliteration and rhyme in a poem

Alliteration is when writers put words together that start with the same sound.

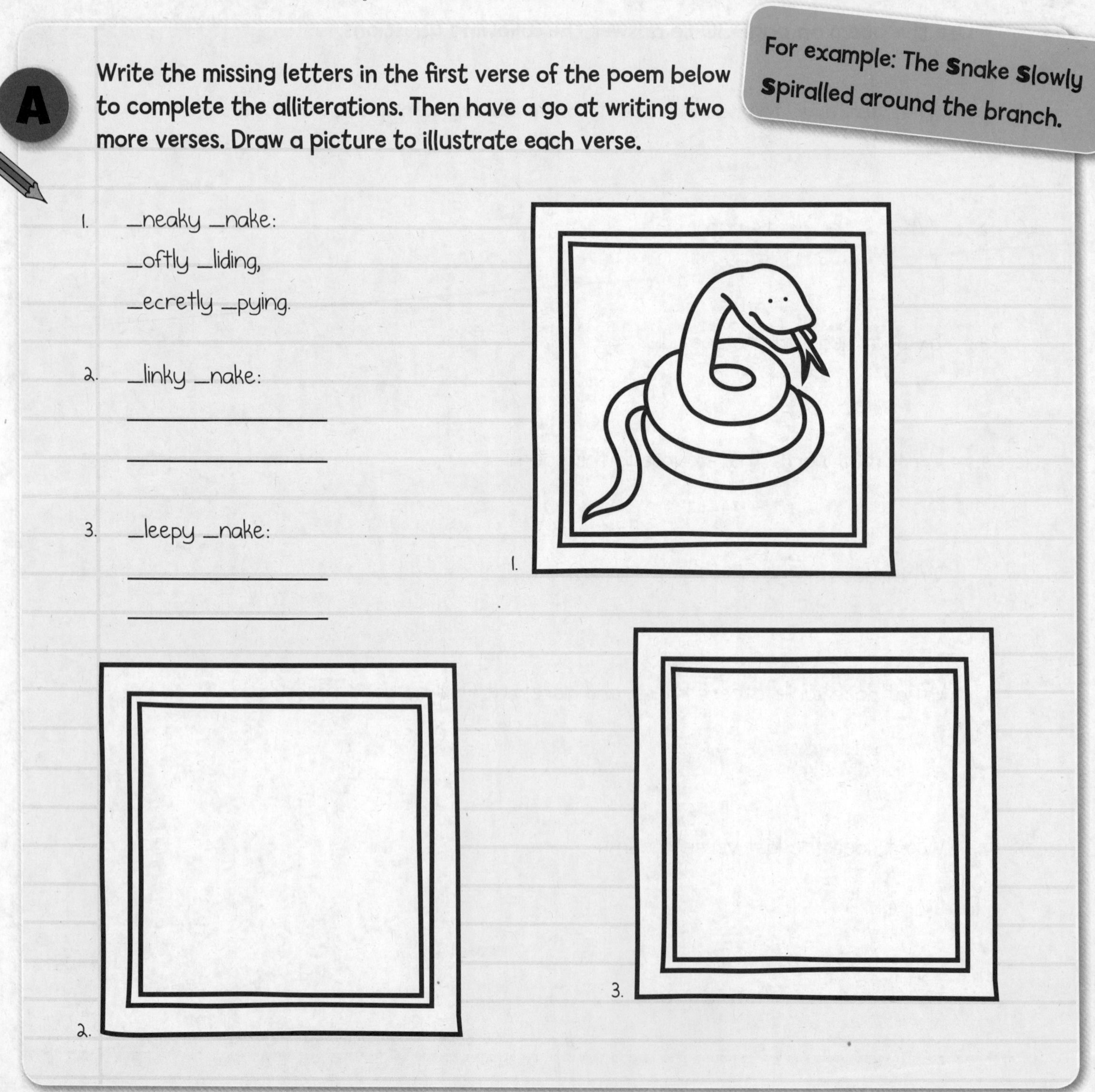

A **Write the missing letters in the first verse of the poem below to complete the alliterations. Then have a go at writing two more verses. Draw a picture to illustrate each verse.**

For example: The Snake Slowly Spiralled around the branch.

1. _neaky _nake:
   _oftly _liding,
   _ecretly _pying.

2. _linky _nake:
   ____
   ____

3. _leepy _nake:
   ____
   ____

1.

2.

3.

When words end with the same sound, we say that they rhyme. Poets use rhyme to make their poems more memorable and to give the words a pattern.

The Eagle

He clasps the crag with crooked hands;
Close to the sun in lonely lands,
Ringed with the azure world, he stands.

The wrinkled sea beneath him crawls;
He watches from his mountain walls,
And like a thunderbolt he falls.

Alfred, Lord Tennyson (1809–92)

alliteration: Words that start with the same sound, e.g. fox, fire, phone.

rhyme: Words that end with the same sound 'rhyme', e.g. boat and coat, wing and ring.

Read the poem and underline the rhymes. Then read it again and underline the alliterations. Copy the words below to make two lists. Can you add to the lists with words of your own?

Rhymes:	Alliterations:
______________	______________
______________	______________
______________	______________
______________	______________
______________	______________
______________	______________
______________	______________
______________	______________

Playscripts

Learning objective: to understand the layout of a playscript

This is an extract from a play. Read it twice, carefully, and take notice of the way in which it is written - for example, the stage directions are in italics.

Scene 1:
Last Day of Term
Classroom in 31st-century Britain.

Characters:
Narrator
Teacher: Number 1471
Robot Assistant: Bot

Narrator: It was the last day of term. Teacher 1471 and his robot assistant, Bot, were getting ready for the day ahead.

1471: *(yawning)* Good morning, Bot.

Bot: *(entering the date on the touch-screen learning wall)* Greetings, Sir, on this the three hundred and sixty-sixth day of term!

1471: Give out the books please, Bot.

Bot: Do you mean those curious, pre-computer-age page-turners, Sir? We haven't used those for over a thousand years!

1471: I know we haven't, but I thought we'd start with an ancient history lesson today!

A **Rewrite the playscript as an ordinary story text, putting in speech marks and other punctuation. The first few sentences have been done to start you off.**

It was the last day of term. Teacher 1471 and his robot assistant, Bot, were getting ready for the day ahead.

"Good morning, Bot," said 1471, yawning.

Speech marks can be used to break up long sections of speech.

For example, these sections of speech are rather long:

"Do you mean those curious, pre-computer-age page-turners, Sir? We haven't used those for over a thousand years!" **exclaimed Bot.**

"I know we haven't, but I thought we'd start with an ancient history lesson today!" **replied 1471.**

It sounds better to write:

"Do you mean those curious, pre-computer-age page-turners, Sir?" **asked Bot.** "We haven't used those for over a thousand years!"

"I know we haven't," **replied 1471**, "but I thought we'd start with an ancient history lesson today!"

Legends

Learning objective: to be able to extract information from the text of a well-known legend

A legend is a traditional story about a person or an event in history. It is based on truth, but retold to be more exciting. This is an extract from the legend The Trojan Horse. Read it twice, carefully.

The Trojan Horse

The Greeks and the Trojans had been at war for ten years. The Greeks were determined to rescue their queen, Helen, who had been kidnapped by Paris, the Trojan prince. But the Greeks could not break down the walls of Troy.

Odysseus thought up a plan. He ordered a huge wooden horse to be designed so that he and his soldiers could hide inside it. Then the Greek ships sailed away from Troy, leaving behind one man, Sinon, and the wooden horse. The ships lay in wait…

When the Trojans saw the Greeks sail away they thought they had won the war, but they were suspicious when they saw the horse. Sinon persuaded them that it would bring them luck.

So the Trojans dragged the horse into the city. That night they had a huge celebration until finally everyone fell asleep. Sinon released the door in the belly of the horse and Odysseus and his soldiers poured out. The Trojans were killed in their beds and the gates of Troy were opened to the Greeks, who had returned in their ships. Finally, Helen was rescued and Troy was destroyed.

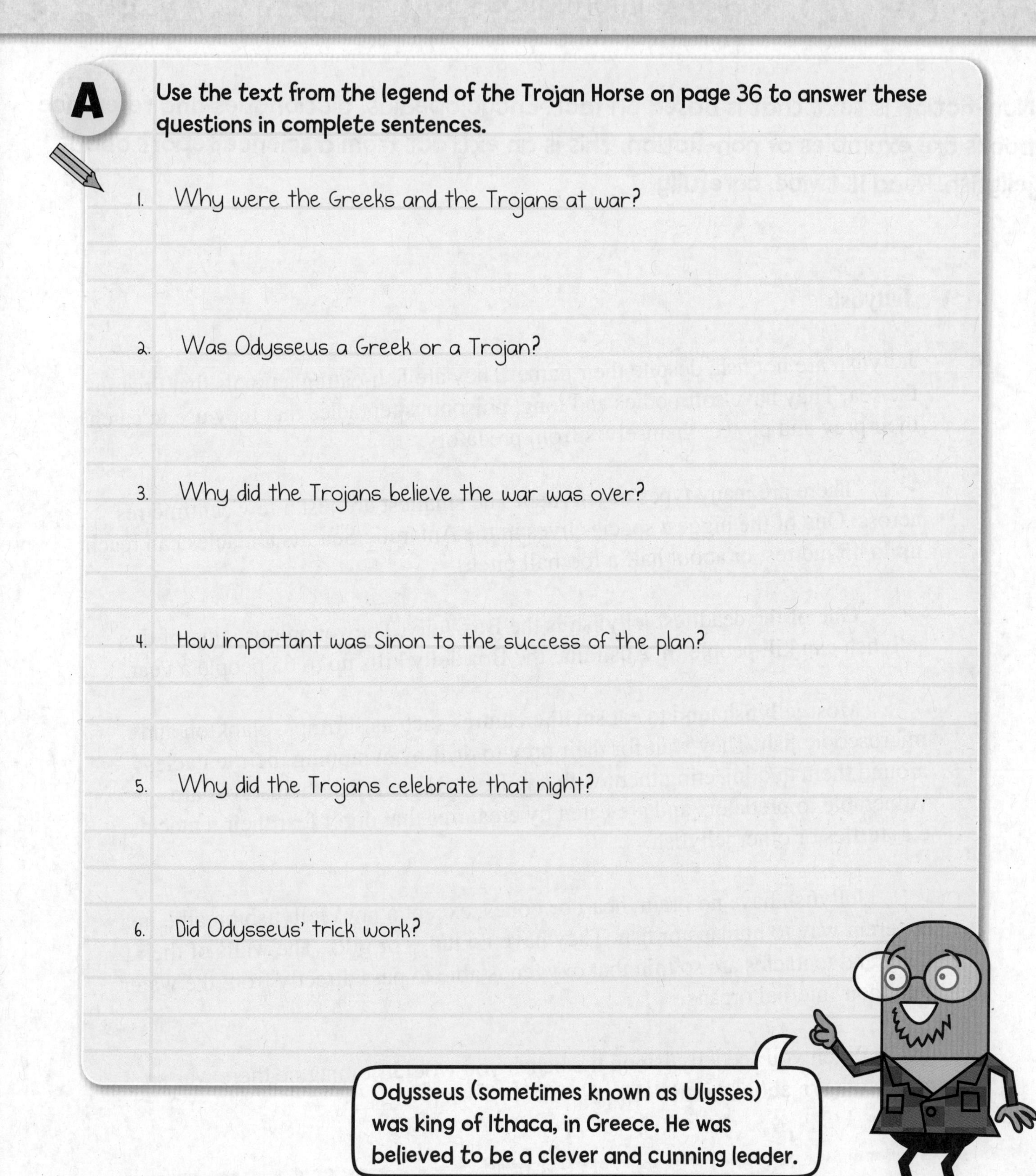

A

Use the text from the legend of the Trojan Horse on page 36 to answer these questions in complete sentences.

1. Why were the Greeks and the Trojans at war?

2. Was Odysseus a Greek or a Trojan?

3. Why did the Trojans believe the war was over?

4. How important was Sinon to the success of the plan?

5. Why did the Trojans celebrate that night?

6. Did Odysseus' trick work?

Odysseus (sometimes known as Ulysses) was king of Ithaca, in Greece. He was believed to be a clever and cunning leader.

Reports and information

Learning objective: to read and understand non-fiction texts and retrieve information

Non-fiction is text that is based on fact. Encyclopedias, dictionaries and reference books are examples of non-fiction. This is an extract from a science report about jellyfish. Read it twice, carefully.

Jellyfish

Jellyfish are not fish, despite their name. They are fish-eating animals that float in the sea. They have soft bodies and long, poisonous tentacles that they use to catch their prey and protect themselves from predators.

There are many types of jellyfish. The smallest are just a few centimetres across. One of the biggest species lives in the Antarctic Sea. Its tentacles can reach up to 45 metres, or about half a football pitch!

One of the deadliest jellyfish is the Box Jelly. The venomous sting of this jellyfish can kill people. In Australia, the Box Jelly kills up to 65 people a year.

Most jellyfish tend to eat small creatures such as shrimps, plankton and microscopic fish. They wait for their prey to drift by, wrapping their tentacles around them and injecting them with a poison. But jellyfish themselves are vulnerable to predators and are eaten by creatures that don't fear their tentacles, e.g. turtles or other jellyfish.

Jellyfish have no brain, heart or bones, except a jaw! Jellyfish breathe in a different way to humans or fish. They have no lungs or gills. The walls of their body and tentacles are so thin that oxygen is able to pass directly from the water into their internal organs.

When you see jellyfish on the beach you wouldn't imagine there was so much to learn about them!

Answer these questions in full sentences.

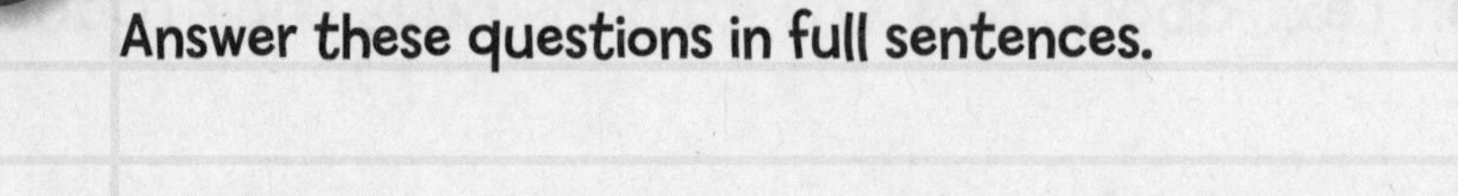

1. Where is one of the biggest species of jellyfish found?

2. Which is one of the most deadly jellyfish?

3. What do jellyfish eat?

4. To which creatures are jellyfish prey?

Try doing some of your own research on another sea creature, and write a paragraph below explaining anything interesting you have found out.

Rewrite, in your own words, any information you find. Don't just copy the text.

DEFINITION

prey: An animal that is hunted by another animal for food.

predator: An animal that hunts another animal.

Explanation text

Learning objective: to read and understand explanation texts and retrieve information

Writing that explains who, what, when, where, why and how is called explanation text. This is a piece of explanation text about how the Romans built their roads. Read it twice, carefully.

How were Roman roads built?

The Romans were famous road builders. Some of the roads they built are still being used today, over 2000 years later. So how did they build their roads to last this long?

First of all, they would look for the straightest route between two points. The trees and shrubs were cleared and a ditch one metre deep was dug. The ditch was filled with three layers.

The first layer, at the bottom of the ditch, was made up of big stones. This was to prevent the road from sinking.

On top of this, making up the second layer, they put small broken stones, pebbles, sand and cement.

For the third layer, they cut large, flat paving stones out of hard rock and set these tightly together in concrete to make the surface of the road. The road was slightly curved at the top so that rain water would drain off.

Finally, the edge of the road was lined with upright kerbstones. Major roads had ditches cut on each side.

DEFINITION

Roman: A soldier or a citizen who came from the ancient city of Rome, in Italy.

Diagrams and charts are often drawn alongside explanation text to make the meaning clearer.

A Use the text on page 40 to draw a diagram that shows how a Roman road was built. Use the text below to label your diagram clearly.

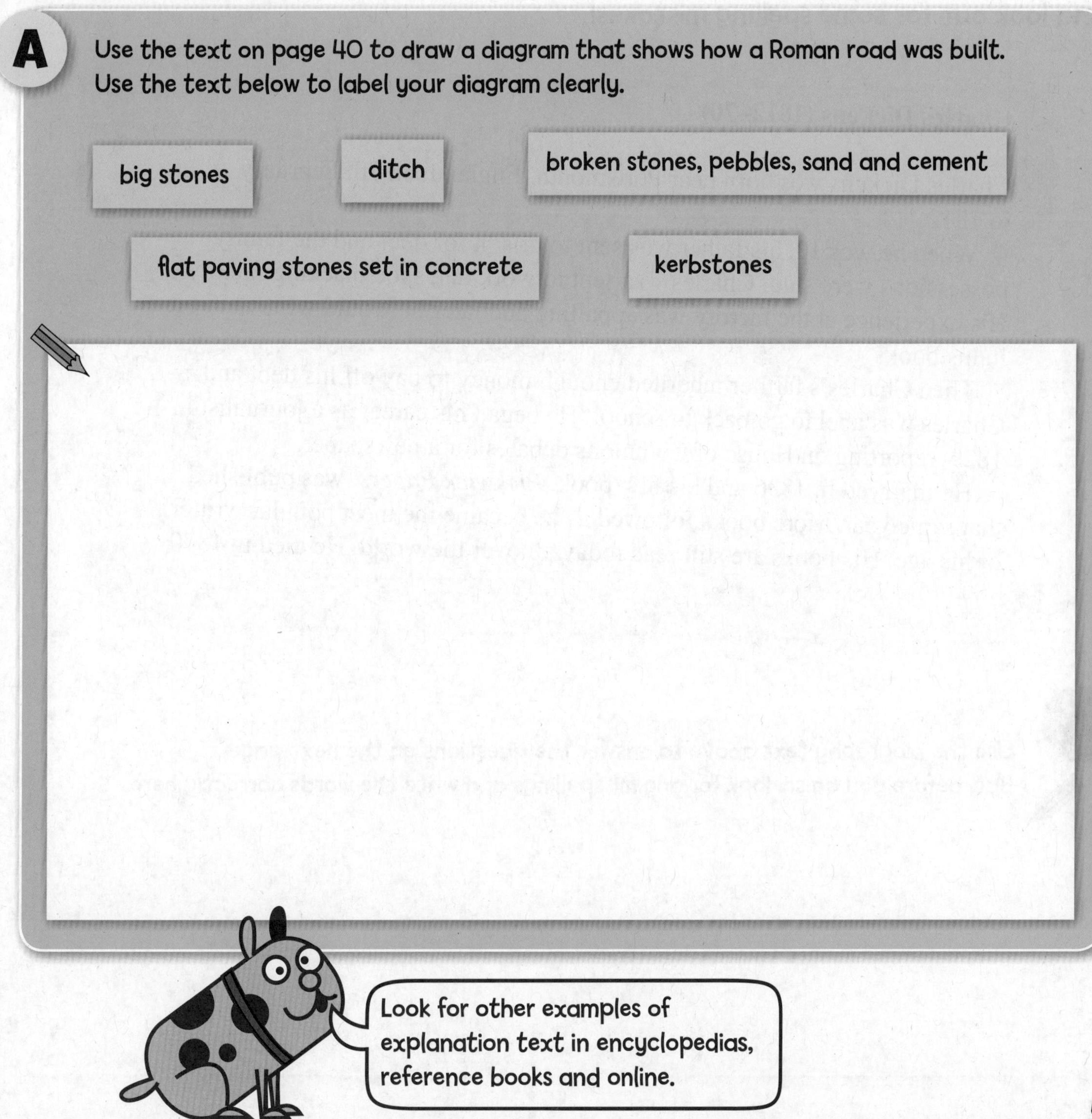

Biography

Learning objective: to read and understand biography text

A book, or a piece of writing, that is an account of a person's life is called a biography. This is a biography of Charles Dickens. Read it twice, carefully, and look out for some spelling mistakes!

Charles Dickens (1812–70)

Charles Dickens wos born near Portsmouth, England, on 7th February in 1812.

When he wos 12, his father wos sent to prison for debt and the family possessions were sold. Charles was sent to work in a shoe blacking factory. His experience at the factory was appalling and later he would write about it in his books.

Then Charles's farther inherited enough money to pay off his debt and Charles was abel to go back to school. He began his career as a journalist in 1829, reporting on House of Commons debates for a newspaper.

He marryed in 1836 and his first book, *Pickwick Papers*, was published that same year. More books followed as he became the most popular writter of his age. His books are still read today all over the world. He died in 1870.

A

Use the biography text above to answer the questions on the next page. But, before you do so, look for any misspellings and write the words correctly here.

B **Use the biography text about Charles Dickens to answer these questions in complete sentences.**

1. How old was Charles Dickens when he died?

2. Why do you think dates are important in a biography?

3. What was Charles doing on each of these dates? (Next to each date write some information taken from the text on page 42.)
   1812: ____________________
   1824: ____________________
   1829: ____________________
   1836: ____________________
   1870: ____________________

4. Write a short biography below of someone you admire or know well. Try to include some important dates.

Formal letters

Learning objective: to read formal letters of complaint and understand how to write them

This is a formal letter of complaint. Read it twice, carefully.

3 Park Road
Newtown
Cheshire
CH32 5RS
United Kingdom

Marco Martino
Manager
Excellenti Hotel
Naples
Italy

8th May 2014

Dear Mr Martino,

I am writing to complain about the lack of service and poor quality of the Excellenti Hotel.

Firstly, we spent the greater part of our two-week holiday waiting to be served in the restaurant. When our meals finally arrived each day, they were cold and inedible.

Secondly, we had booked a luxury family room with a sea view, but found ourselves in a cupboard that was not big enough to swing a cat in, although we had a wonderful view of the rubbish bins.

Thirdly, the swimming pool was more like an over-sized bathtub – hardly big enough for four guests, let alone the forty guests who were booked in at the hotel.

Finally, the cicadas made a deafening din, waking us up at dawn each day. No mention was made of these other noisy guests in the brochure.

I hope you agree that this is not the kind of service one would expect of the five-star Excellenti Hotel, and trust that you will offer us compensation for the disappointment this has caused us.

Yours sincerely,

I. M. Notamused
Mrs I. M. Notamused

A

Now have a go at answering these questions about the letter.

1. What do you think the word 'inedible' means?
2. Find an example of sarcasm in the letter and copy it here.
3. Underline the words in the letter used to connect the paragraphs (the connectives).
4. Circle an example of a metaphor.
5. Is there anything about the holiday that the manager could not have changed?
6. In which city was the hotel?

A formal letter is always laid out in the same way. Use the template on the right as a guide when you are writing a formal letter.

Write a short letter to the manager expressing the opposite viewpoint about the Excellenti Hotel.

Your address and the date

The person you are writing to and their address

Dear Mr/Mrs/Ms/Miss ________________,

Use formal language, eg: I am writing ...

Write in the first person, using **I**, **my**, **mine** and **we**.

Yours sincerely,

____

Writing poems

Learning objective: to write a poem based on a given structure

Fiction is writing that comes from your imagination. Poems, fairy tales, adventure stories and playscripts are all types of fiction.

A haiku is a traditional Japanese poem that has a total of 17 syllables arranged in three lines: 5, 7, 5.

For example:

Brilliant blue sky	Brill/i/ant/ blue/ sky
Trees dressed in emerald green	Trees/ dressed/ in/ em/er/ald/ green
Now that summer's here.	Now/ that/ summ/er's/ here.

'Dog' has one syllable, 'donkey' has two syllables and 'dinosaur' has three syllables.

A Have a go at completing this haiku about autumn.

_________ / _________ / _________ / _________ / sky
Trees _________ / _________ / _________ / _________ / _________ / _________
Now that autumn's here.

B Then try spring and winter following the same '5, 7, 5' haiku format.

____
____
____

____
____
____

A kenning is a kind of word puzzle or riddle. It is a way of talking about something without using its name.

Here are two examples:

Blood-sucker People-biter Loud-buzzer.	Noisy-barker Tail-wagger Bone-eater.

Can you work out what each kenning is about?

C Try writing some kennings of your own below. Choose an animal or a familiar object. Test them out on a friend.

All good writers use their senses to describe what they can see or imagine.

D Use your senses to complete the senses poem below.

I'd love to taste:
A crunchy potato crisp, lightly sprinkled with sea salt and black pepper.
I'd love to see:

___

I'd love to hear:

___

I'd love to touch:

___

I'd love to smell:

___

Sentences and paragraphs

Learning objective: to rearrange sentence order and divide text into paragraphs

In good writing, the sentences don't all follow the same pattern. If they did, the writing would sound dull.

If you change the order of words in a sentence, you can keep your writing lively and interesting. Which of these word orders do you like best?

1. As the thunder crashed, Jack saw a tall tree looming up from the shadows.
2. Jack saw, as the thunder crashed, a tall tree looming up from the shadows.
3. Jack saw a tall tree looming up from the shadows, as the thunder crashed.

A

Find two different ways to rewrite each of the sentences below. Use the same words but add any commas you need.

1. A crow, big and black, screeched in the darkness.

2. Jack, startled, held his breath.

3. He realized, with horror, a creature was creeping towards him.

4. A church bell rang close by, like some kind of terrible warning.

DEFINITION

paragraph: A group of sentences about the same subject.

Writers put sentences that are about the same subject into groups called paragraphs. It helps readers make sense of the writing.

Paragraph rules

- Group sentences together that are about the same idea, place, action or person.
- In a story, start a fresh paragraph when something new happens.
- Leave a blank line between paragraphs.
- Start a new paragraph about 2cm in from the margin, so it is easy to spot.

B

Below, the writing is squashed up into one paragraph, making it hard to read. It should be spread out into three paragraphs. Draw two vertical lines in two places where you think new paragraphs should start.

Jack started to run. He ran down the hill and along the hedge, looking for the gate. It was there somewhere, but in the dark, he just couldn't find it. He knew he didn't have much time. "I wonder where Jack is," said his mother, looking anxiously at the kitchen clock. "He's going to be late for his tea!" The thing on the hill lifted its head to gaze at the moon. It snuffled the cold, clear air. Then it let out a long, blood-curdling howl and lumbered after Jack.

C

In each of these paragraphs, there is one sentence in the wrong place. Underline the sentence that belongs in the other paragraph.

Jack's scrabbling fingers found the latch of the gate. It was rusty and stiff. He rattled it hard, but it wouldn't shift. Long, sticky drool slobbered from its jaws. He'd have to climb over instead.

Its breath came in clouds as it blundered down the hill. Great, stinking clouds, that smelled like rotting cabbage. He glanced anxiously over his shoulder. Its coarse black hair stood up stiffly, like spines.

Writing story settings

Learning objective: to recognize different settings, and write a story setting

The setting is where and when a story takes place. Describing the setting can create mood and atmosphere.

A **Draw lines to match the settings below to the appropriate stories on the right.**

1. Fairytale castle or forest
2. School or home
3. Old house or graveyard at night
4. Remote or faraway place
5. Other planets

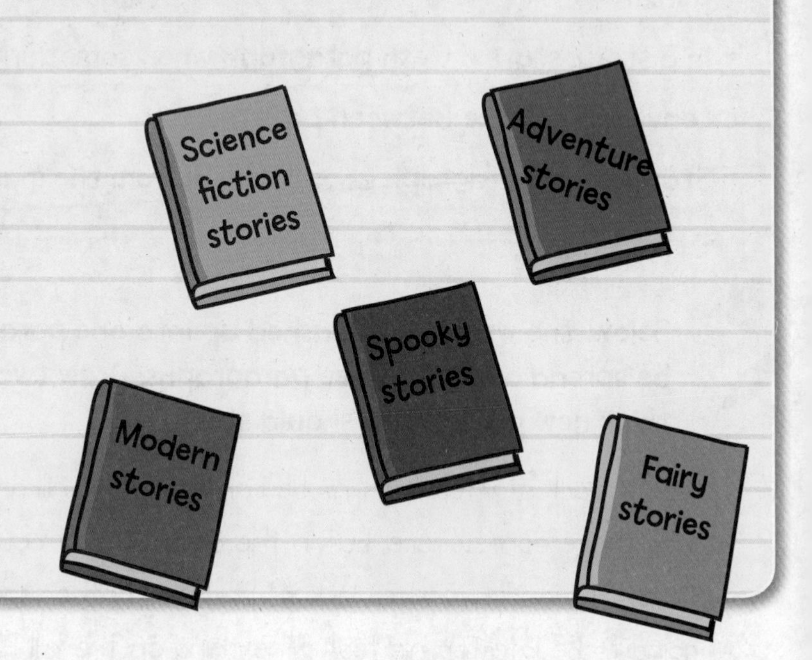

B **Read the passage below. Circle the words that tell you where and when this story is set.**

The summer sun is high in the sky. The crashing waves break against my chest as I race towards them with my board. In front of me, I hear my friends shouting and I taste excitement in the salty air.

DEFINITION

atmosphere: This is the feeling you create for the reader. It can be scary, funny, mysterious and so on.

remote: A faraway, lonely place.

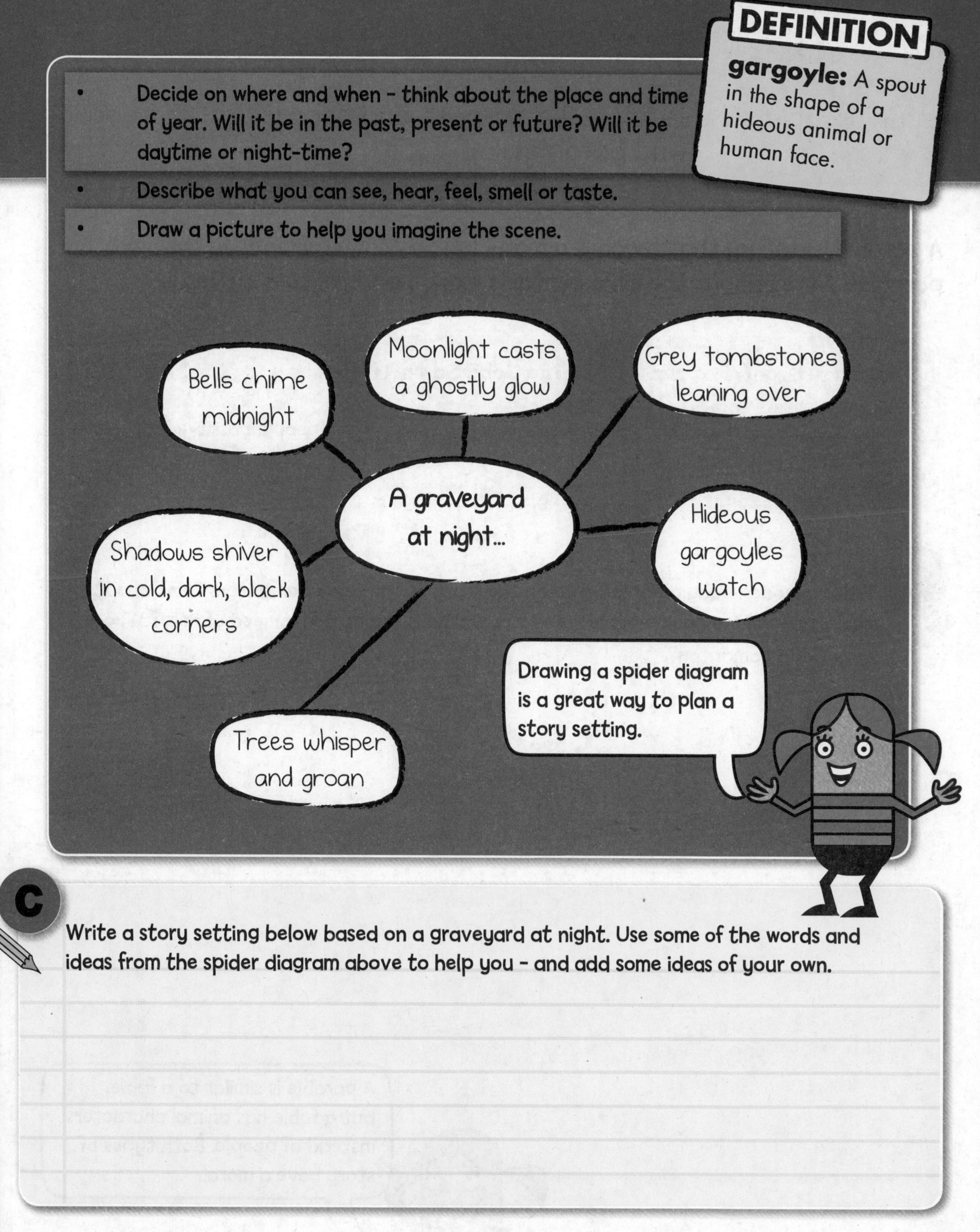
DEFINITION
gargoyle: A spout in the shape of a hideous animal or human face.
Decide on where and when - think about the place and time of year. Will it be in the past, present or future? Will it be daytime or night-time?
Describe what you can see, hear, feel, smell or taste.
Draw a picture to help you imagine the scene.
A graveyard at night...
Bells chime midnight
Moonlight casts a ghostly glow
Grey tombstones leaning over
Hideous gargoyles watch
Shadows shiver in cold, dark, black corners
Trees whisper and groan
Drawing a spider diagram is a great way to plan a story setting.
C
Write a story setting below based on a graveyard at night. Use some of the words and ideas from the spider diagram above to help you - and add some ideas of your own.

Writing parables and ballads

Learning objective: to know the purpose and characteristics of ballads and parables

A parable is a story that teaches a moral lesson. Many religious faiths have parables. For example, the Bible contains many parables told by Jesus.

Here is a summary of a parable called **The Good Samaritan.**

A man is attacked and robbed as he walks down the road. Many people pass by, but no one stops to help him. Eventually, a Good Samaritan comes along and helps the man.

A

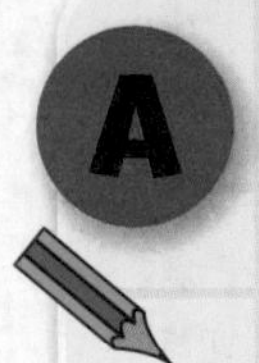

Write a modern-day parable based on the story of The Good Samaritan. Think about the setting where your parable takes place. Who is the person in need of help? Who is your Good Samaritan?

A parable is similar to a fable, but a fable has animal characters instead of people. Both types of story have a moral.

A ballad is a song or poem that tells a story. It has short rhyming verses and often a chorus repeated after each verse.

B Read this ballad. Then fill in the missing rhyming words with words of your own.

Memories of a Norman Soldier

Will I be lucky or will I not
Succeed in helping with William's plot?
Men were facing me with death
My cheeks feel their icy __________.

Chorus:
It was a gory sight
The battle full of death and fright
To see the people suffer so
The victims of the deadly bow!

Now arrows are falling like __________
Surely the Saxons fight in vain
My arrows shoot in to the sky
Towards the enemy they __________.

Harold is now in clear view
In his direction the arrows __________
One has hit him in the __________
For now he shall surely die.

As I watch Harold __________
A tear comes to my weary eye
As I look at what we've done
It's a tragedy, but the war is __________!

By Holly and Natasha (age 11)

Writing instructions

Learning objective: to know how to write clear instructions

Instructions need to be written in a clear and concise way. Sometimes, when it is difficult to explain something in words, you can use a diagram as well.

How to draw a dog

What you need:

- paper
- pencil

What you do:

1. Draw a faint oval outline for the body and a smaller oval for the head.
2. Draw two small ovals for ears and four thin ovals for legs.
3. Within and on top of the oval outlines, draw more realistic dog-like features.
4. Then add details such as a nose, mouth, eyes, tail and spots.

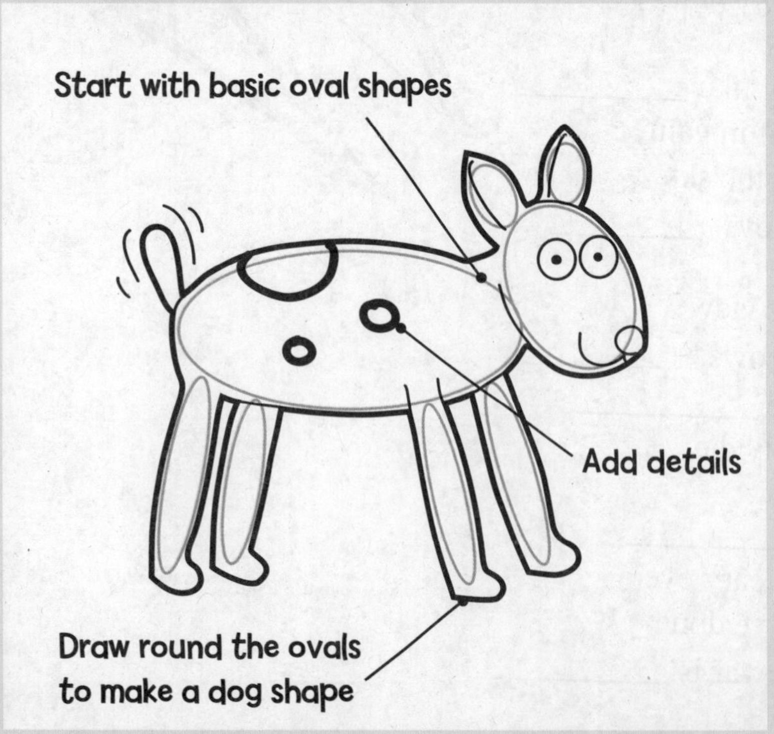

Start with basic oval shapes

Add details

Draw round the ovals to make a dog shape

Add labels and leader lines where necessary to explain your diagram.

DEFINITION

concise: Using as few words as possible to say something.

A craft project

- Write a list of what you are going to need.
- Number the separate points.
- Write step-by-step instructions.
- Draw a diagram if you think it would be helpful.

Remember!
Write in the present tense and second person, using the pronoun 'you'.

A

Write a set of instructions explaining how to build a sandcastle with a moat.

HOW TO BUILD A SANDCASTLE WITH A MOAT

What you need:

- bucket
-
-
-
-
-

What you do:

1. You will need to use wet sand near the water's edge, but not too close or your sandcastle might get washed away before you finish it!
2.
3.
4.
5.

Writing a discussion text

Learning objective: to know how to write a discussion text

Discussion text can be used to bring together all the arguments for and against in a discussion.

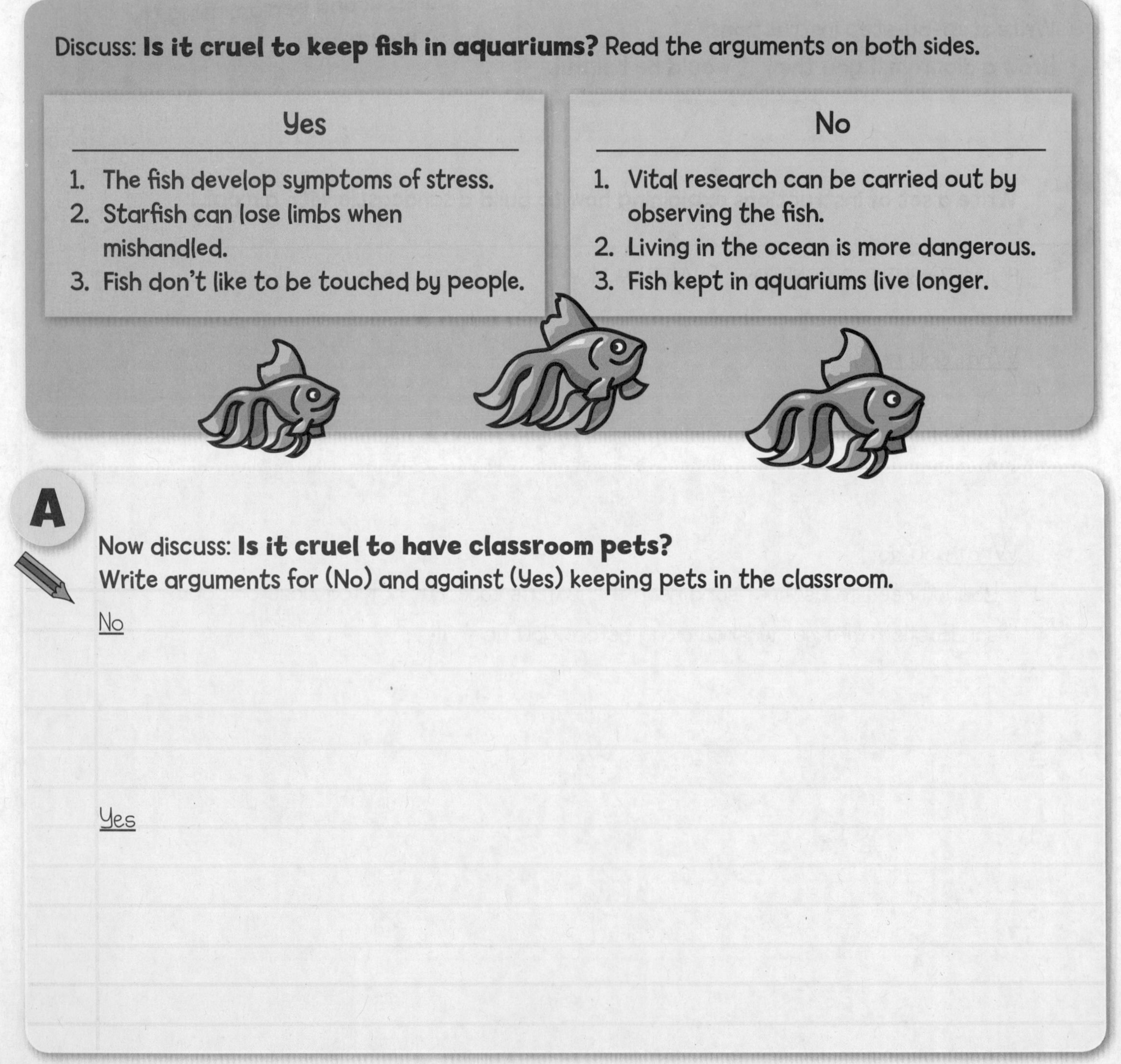

Discuss: **Is it cruel to keep fish in aquariums?** Read the arguments on both sides.

Yes	No
1. The fish develop symptoms of stress.	1. Vital research can be carried out by observing the fish.
2. Starfish can lose limbs when mishandled.	2. Living in the ocean is more dangerous.
3. Fish don't like to be touched by people.	3. Fish kept in aquariums live longer.

A

Now discuss: **Is it cruel to have classroom pets?**
Write arguments for (No) and against (Yes) keeping pets in the classroom.

No

Yes